Editor
Tracy Edmunds

Editorial Project Manager
Mara Ellen Guckian

Managing Editors
Karen Goldfluss, M.S. Ed.
Ina Massler Levin, M.A.

Illustrator
Kevin McCarthy

Cover Artist
Denise Bauer

Art Manager
Kevin Barnes

Art Director
CJae Froshay

Imaging
Rosa C. See

Publisher
Mary D. Smith, M.S. Ed.

Math Games

Grades Pre•K–K

- Number Recognition and Counting
- Money
- Sequencing Numbers

Authors

Bridget Kilroy Hoffman

Julie R. Mauer, M.A.

Teacher Created Resources, Inc.

6421 Industry Way
Westminster, CA 92683
www.teachercreated.com

ISBN-1-4206-3177-2

Table of Contents

Introduction 3

Helpful Hints 4

Game Assembly and Storage 4

Nature Number Recognition and Counting *(1–20)*

Picnic Party 5

Look Ladybugs! 23

Field of Flowers 41

Buzzing Bees 59

Sizzling Summer Coin Values

Searching for Seashells 77

Lemonade Stand 87

Sand Treasures 97

Scuba Dive 107

Critters Number Sequencing *(1–20)*

Cuddles the Cow 117

Tracy the Turtle 131

Tommy the Tiger 145

Zack the Zebra 159

Parent Letter 173

Instructions for Family Fun Math Games 174

Game Labels 175

Introduction

Full-Color Math Games is a collection of colorful and captivating math board games that will energize any math curriculum and liven up learning for young students. Unlike other resource books on the market, *Full-Color Math Games* is designed for creative pre-kindergarten and kindergarten teachers who strive to provide students with more than just worksheets for math practice and review. While worksheet-based resource books are easy to reproduce and implement in a classroom, they do not bring learning to life! Learning comes to life with *Full-Color Math Games*. This book offers solid, objective-based games for reinforcing math concepts while giving your students an enjoyable way to practice and demonstrate their knowledge. This valuable teacher resource is organized by theme and concept. Each theme is relevant to the interests of young learners, and the concepts covered are precursors for national math standards and benchmarks expected in future grades.

Number and Operations

- Count with understanding.
- Recognize and make comparisons of "how many" in sets of objects.
- Use numbers to describe "how many" are in a set (1 through 20).
- Use one-to-one correspondence.
- Use language such as *before* and *after* to describe position in a sequence of numbers.
- Sequence whole numbers to 20.
- Identify coins by name: *penny, nickel, dime,* and *quarter*.
- Identify coins by value: penny, nickel, dime, and quarter.

Algebra

- Recognize and name numerals through 20.
- Recognize and describe relationships between whole numbers through 20.
- Understand and apply the terms *before, after,* and *between* to numbers through 20.
- Order sets of numbers through 20.

These full-color, fun-filled math games are easy to make. Just follow the simple directions outlined in the *Preparation* section for each game to create great activities that can be used in the classroom in a matter of minutes. You determine how your students will use the games, be it with partners, in small groups, as center activities, one-on-one for student assessment, or as take-home practice for family fun. Any way you choose to use them, *Full-Color Math Games* will provide both variety and consistency for your students while reinforcing everyday math skills. Incorporate these games into an already existing math curriculum or share them with parents to use at home and be rewarded as math comes to life for young students.

Helpful Hints

Full-Color Math Games is extremely versatile and provides teachers with multiple options for use in the classroom.

- **Small group:** Three or four students play together or with the teacher.

- **Partners:** Two students play together.

- **Center activities:** Students can play independently or with partners. Place the games in a math center to reinforce whole-group math instruction on the same concept, or mix and match the games for use with a spiraling curriculum.

- **Practice and review:** Utilize all games on a particular concept with as many as 16 students at the same time. Turn a math period into Game Time!

- **Individual assessment:** Assign one student to complete a game independently, then check the game to assess student progress.

- **Family fun:** Send the game home with students for further enhancement of math skills.

The directions for each of the games in each section are similar. When you introduce one game in the set, students can easily transition to the other games with little or no further assistance. Students can even teach other students how to play.

Game Assembly and Storage

All of the games in *Full-Color Math Games* are easy to make. Below are just a few suggestions on how to prepare and store them.

- Using a color photocopy machine, copy the games and keep the original book as your master, OR dismantle the entire book by separating the pages on the perforated lines, then copy the direction cards and manipulative pages for future reference. Create each game as outlined in the *Preparation* section for the game.

- Assemble the full-color game board by taping the two pages together. Mount the game board on a 12" x 18" piece of construction paper, oak tag, poster board, or file folder. Laminate for durability.

- Laminate and cut out all necessary game pieces such as counting cards, picture cards, cover ups, and direction cards. The cover ups for each game may be cut out as cards or on the picture outline. (Note: Extra cover ups are provided for each game.)

- Store counting cards, picture cards, game boards, and direction cards in resealable storage bags. Label each bag with the game name label provided in the back of this book (page 175), and attach each storage bag of game pieces to its game board.

- Organize the entire collection of board games in plastic file boxes, durable magazine/book holders, desktop file holders, or see-through plastic envelopes with button and string fasteners or Velcro® closures.

Picnic Party

Number Recognition and Counting

Objective: Students will recognize numbers and count sets of objects (1–20) using one-to-one correspondence.

Preparation

1. Assemble and laminate the Picnic Party Game Board (pages 8 and 9).

2. Laminate and cut out the Picnic Party Food Counting Cards (pages 11, 13, 15, 17, and 19).

3. Laminate and cut out the Picnic Party Ant Cover Ups (page 21).

4. Cut out and laminate the Picnic Party Directions (page 5).

5. Store the Picnic Party Food Counting Cards and Ant Cover Ups in a resealable storage bag. Label the bag with the game name label (page 175).

Picnic Party Directions

Materials

Picnic Party Game Board

Picnic Party Food Counting Cards

Picnic Party Ant Cover Ups

How to Play the Game

2–4 players

1. Shuffle the food counting cards and place them facedown beside the Picnic Party game board.

2. Divide the ants among the players.

3. Take turns drawing a food counting card and counting the number of food objects shown on the card. Use an ant to cover the correct answer on the Picnic Party game board.

4. Continue taking turns until all the numbers on the Picnic Party game board have been covered.

PICNIC PARTY

Picnic Party Food Counting Cards

Picnic Party Food Counting Cards

Picnic
Party

Picnic
Party

Picnic
Party

Picnic
Party

Picnic Party Food Counting Cards

Picnic Party Food Counting Cards

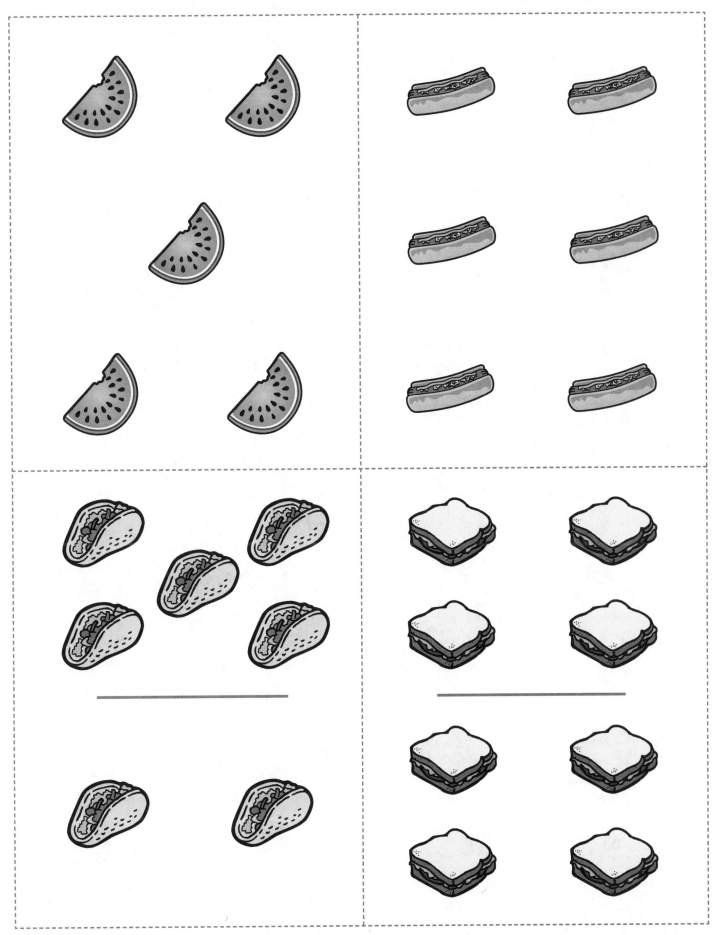

Picnic Party Food Counting Cards

Picnic
Party

Picnic
Party

Picnic
Party

Picnic
Party

Picnic Party Food Counting Cards

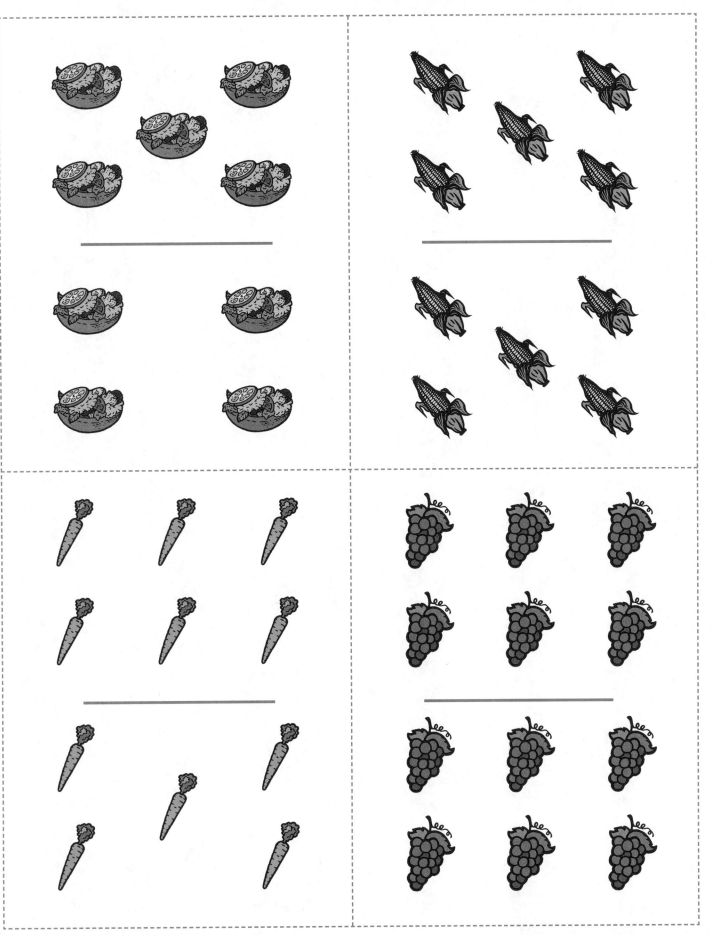

Picnic Party Food Counting Cards

Picnic
Party

Picnic
Party

Picnic
Party

Picnic
Party

Picnic Party Food Counting Cards

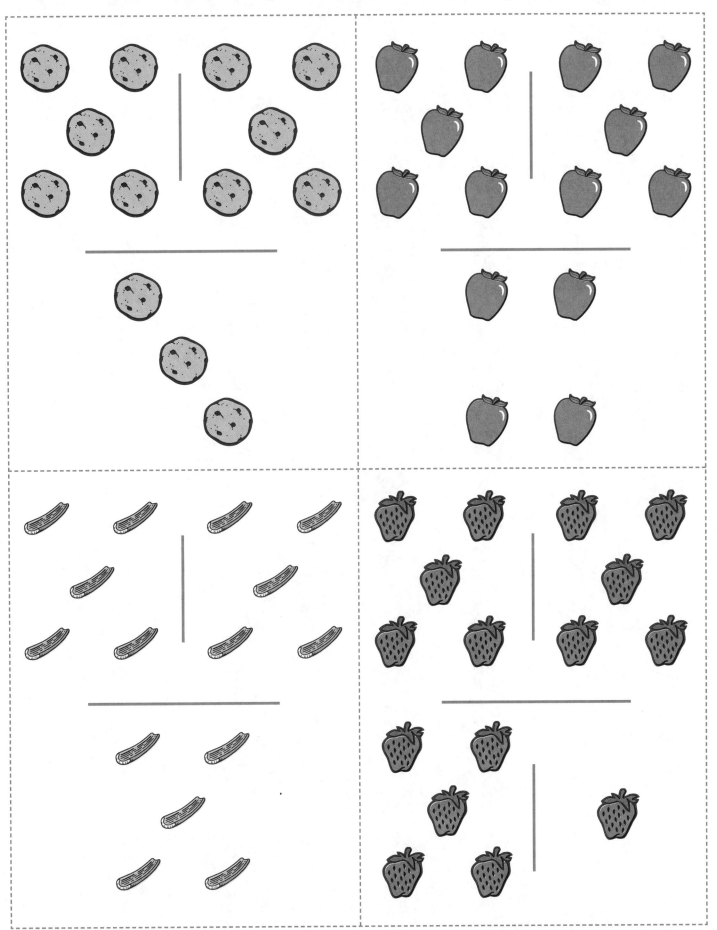

Picnic Party Food Counting Cards

Picnic
Party

Picnic
Party

Picnic
Party

Picnic
Party

Picnic Party Food Counting Cards

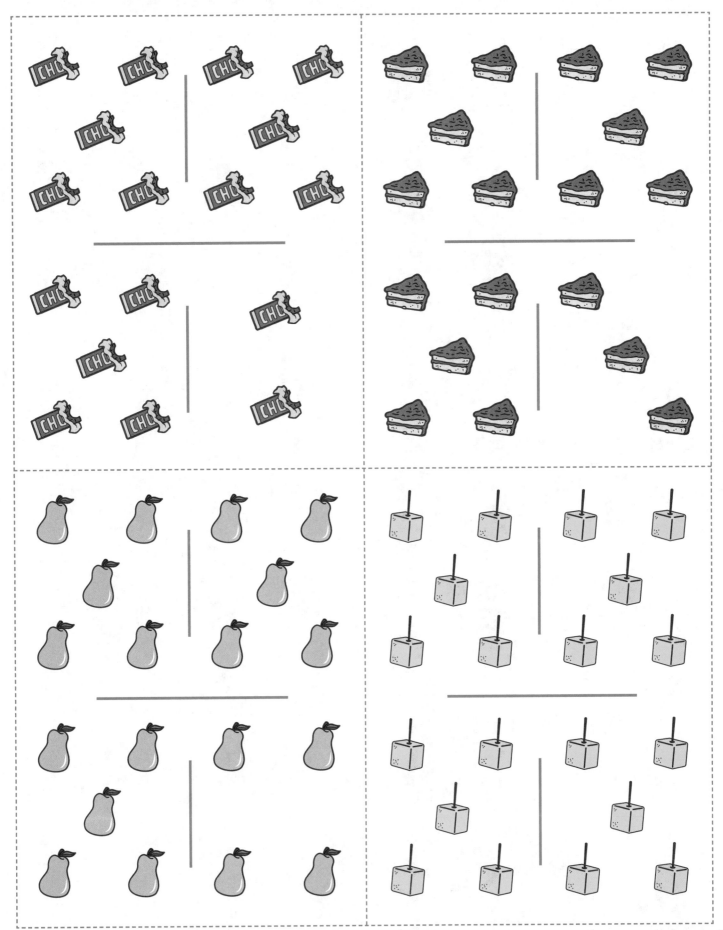

Picnic
Party

Picnic
Party

Picnic
Party

Picnic
Party

Look Ladybugs!

Number Recognition and Counting

Objective: Students will recognize numbers and count sets of objects (1–20) using one-to-one correspondence.

Preparation

1. Assemble and laminate the Look Ladybugs! Ladybugs Game Board (pages 26 and 27).

2. Laminate and cut out the Look Ladybugs! Spots Counting Cards (pages 29, 31, 33, 35, and 37).

3. Laminate and cut out the Look Ladybugs! Ladybugs Cover Ups (page 39).

4. Laminate the Look Ladybugs! Directions (page 23).

5. Store the Look Ladybugs! Spots Counting Cards and Ladybug! Cover Ups in a resealable storage bag. Label the bag with the game name label (page 175).

Look Ladybugs! Directions

Materials

Look Ladybugs! Game Board

Look Ladybugs! Spots Counting Cards

Look Ladybugs! Ladybug Cover Ups

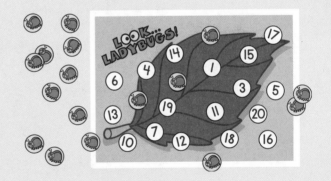

How to Play the Game

2–4 players

1. Shuffle the spots counting cards and place them facedown beside the Look Ladybugs! game board.

2. Divide the ladybugs among the players.

3. Take turns drawing a spots card and counting the number of spots shown on the card. Use a ladybug to cover the correct answer on the Look Ladybugs! game board.

4. Continue taking turns until all the numbers on the Look Ladybugs! game board have been covered.

Look Ladybugs! Spots Counting Cards

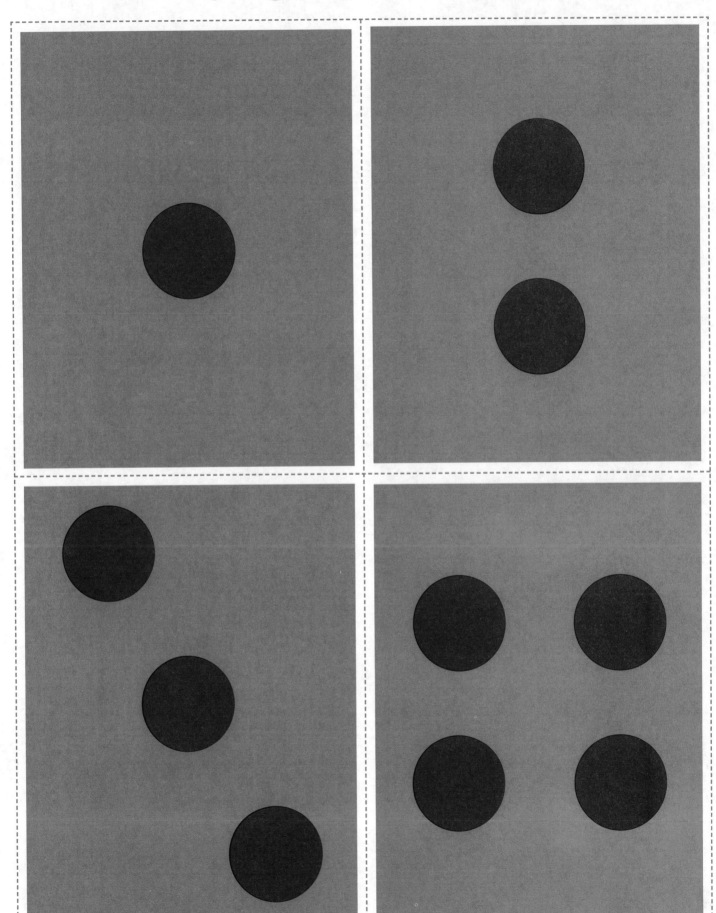

Look
Ladybugs!

Look
Ladybugs!

Look
Ladybugs!

Look
Ladybugs!

Look Ladybugs! Spots Counting Cards

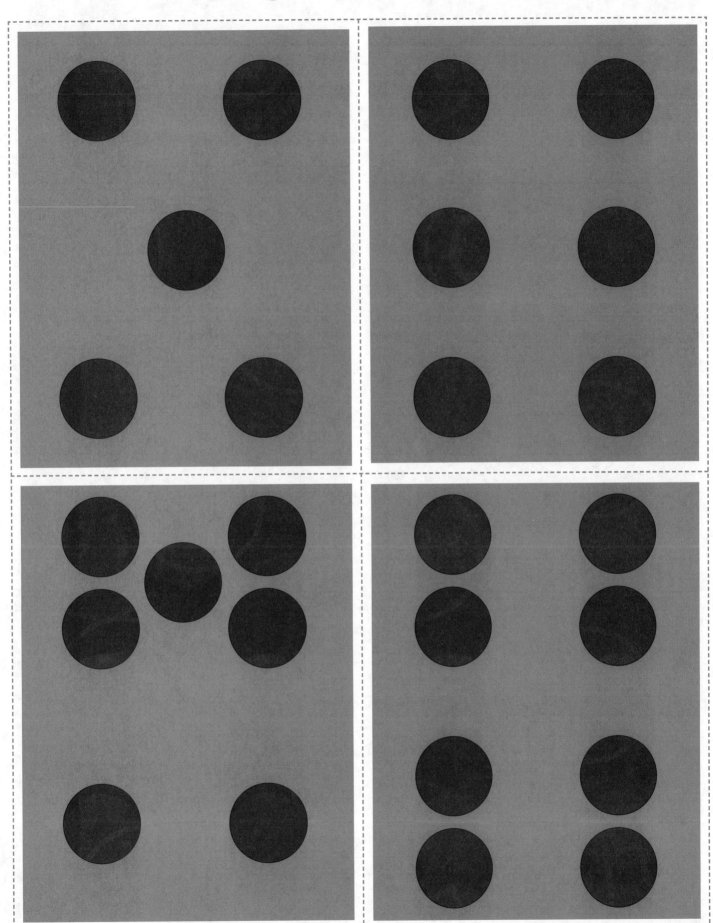

Look
Ladybugs!

Look
Ladybugs!

Look
Ladybugs!

Look
Ladybugs!

Look Ladybugs! Spots Counting Cards

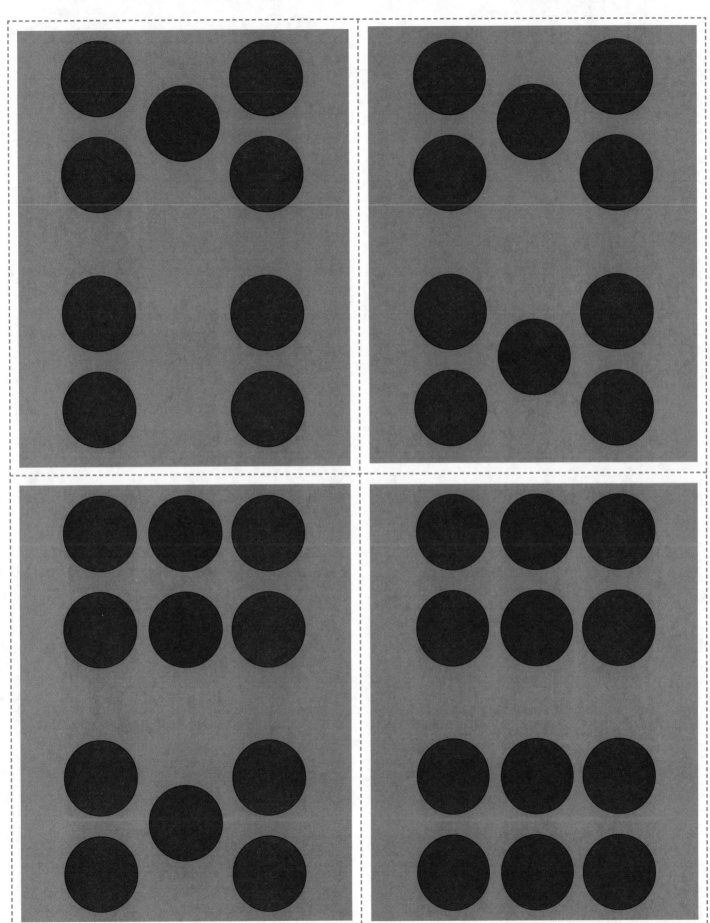

Look
Ladybugs!

Look
Ladybugs!

Look
Ladybugs!

Look
Ladybugs!

Look Ladybugs! Spots Counting Cards

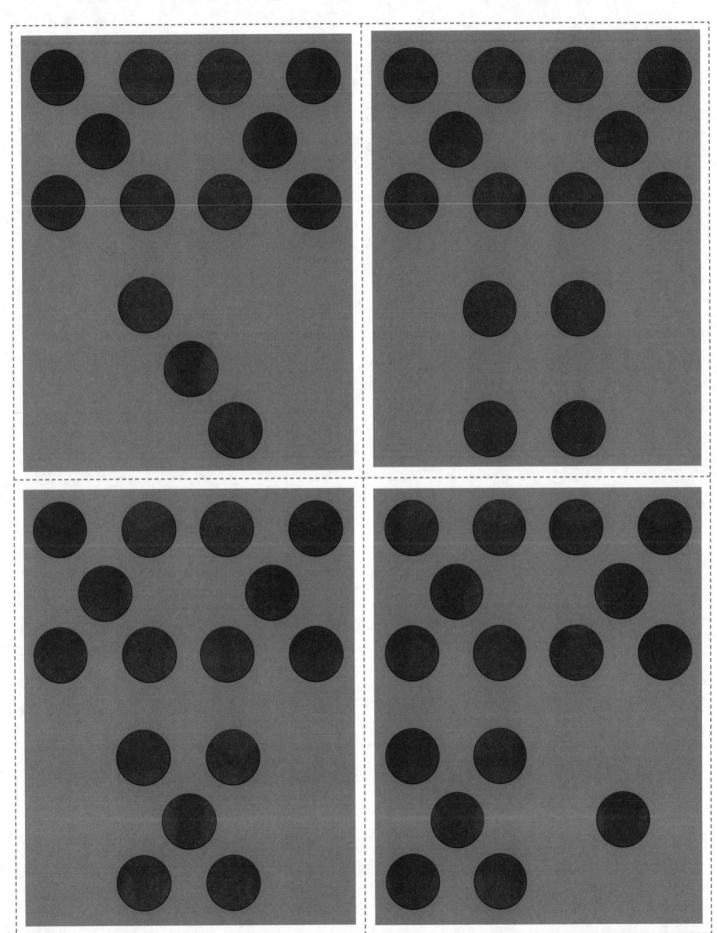

Look
Ladybugs!

Look
Ladybugs!

Look
Ladybugs!

Look
Ladybugs!

Look Ladybugs! Spots Counting Cards

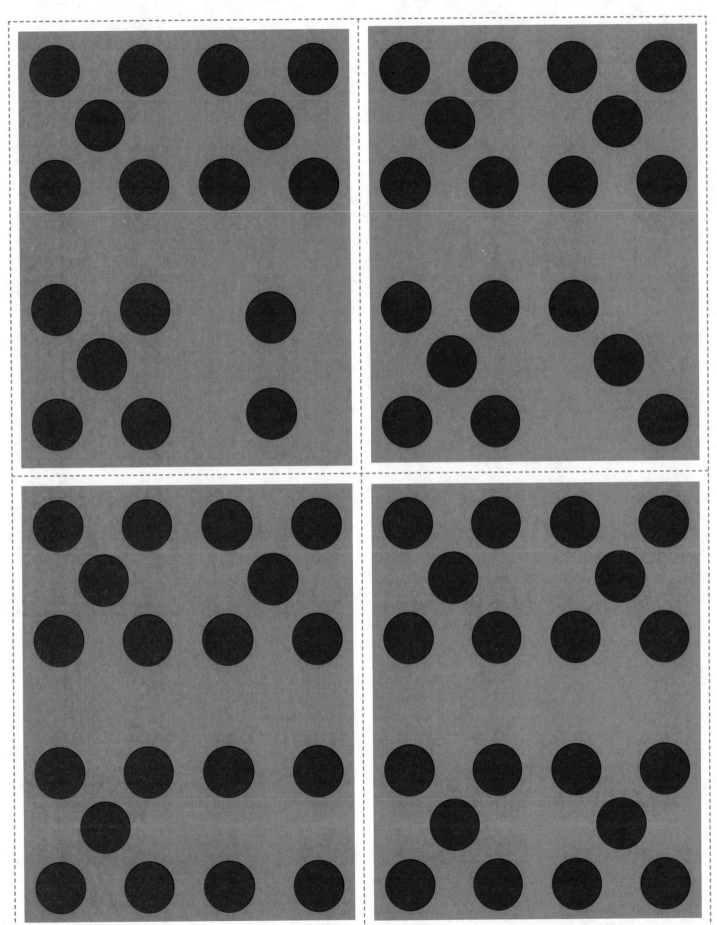

Look
Ladybugs!

Look
Ladybugs!

Look
Ladybugs!

Look
Ladybugs!

Field of Flowers

Number Recognition and Counting

Objective: Students will recognize numbers and count sets of objects (1–20) using one-to-one correspondence.

Preparation

1. Assemble and laminate the Field of Flowers Game Board (pages 44 and 45).

2. Laminate and cut out the Field of Flowers Flower Counting Cards (pages 47, 49, 51, 53, and 55).

3. Laminate and cut out the Butterfly Cover Ups (page 57).

4. Laminate the Field of Flowers Directions (page 41).

5. Store the Field of Flowers Flower Counting Cards and the Butterfly Cover Ups in a resealable storage bag. Label the bag with the game name label (page 175).

Field of Flowers Directions

Materials

Field of Flowers Game Board
Field of Flowers Flower Counting Cards
Field of Flowers Butterfly Cover Ups

How to Play the Game

2–4 players

1. Shuffle the flower counting cards and place them facedown beside the Field of Flowers game board.

2. Divide the butterflies among the players.

3. Take turns drawing a flower counting card and counting the number of flowers shown on the card. Use a butterfly to cover the correct answer on the Field of Flowers game board.

4. Continue taking turns until all the numbers on the Field of Flowers game board have been covered.

Field of Flowers Counting Cards

Field of Flowers Counting Cards

Field

of

Flowers

Field

of

Flowers

Field

of

Flowers

Field

of

Flowers

Field of Flowers Counting Cards

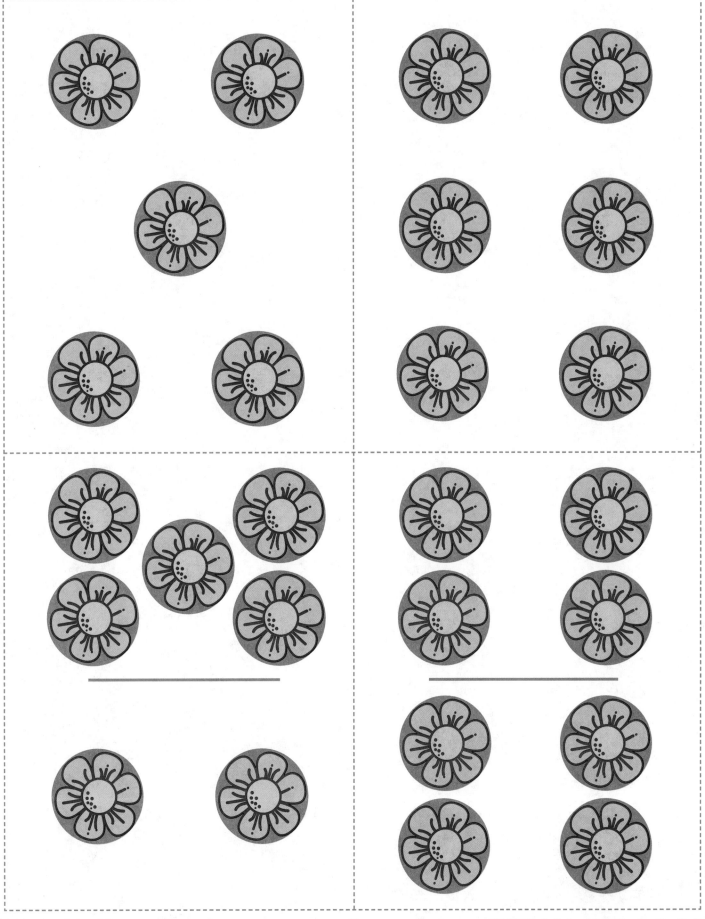

Field of Flowers Counting Cards

Field
of
Flowers

Field
of
Flowers

Field
of
Flowers

Field
of
Flowers

Field of Flowers Counting Cards

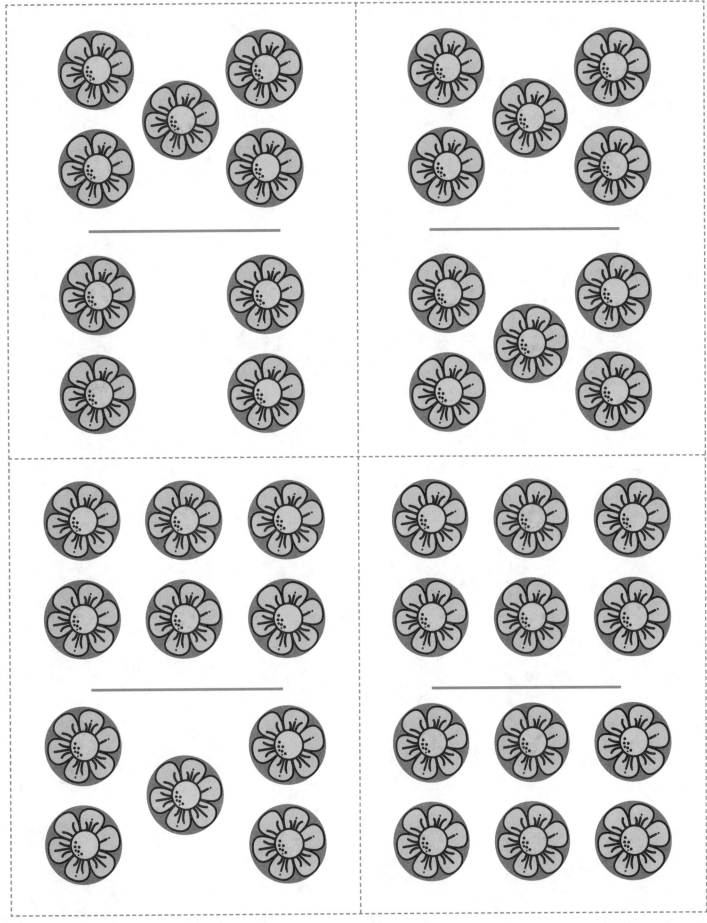

Field of Flowers Counting Cards

Field
of
Flowers

Field
of
Flowers

Field
of
Flowers

Field
of
Flowers

Field of Flowers Counting Cards

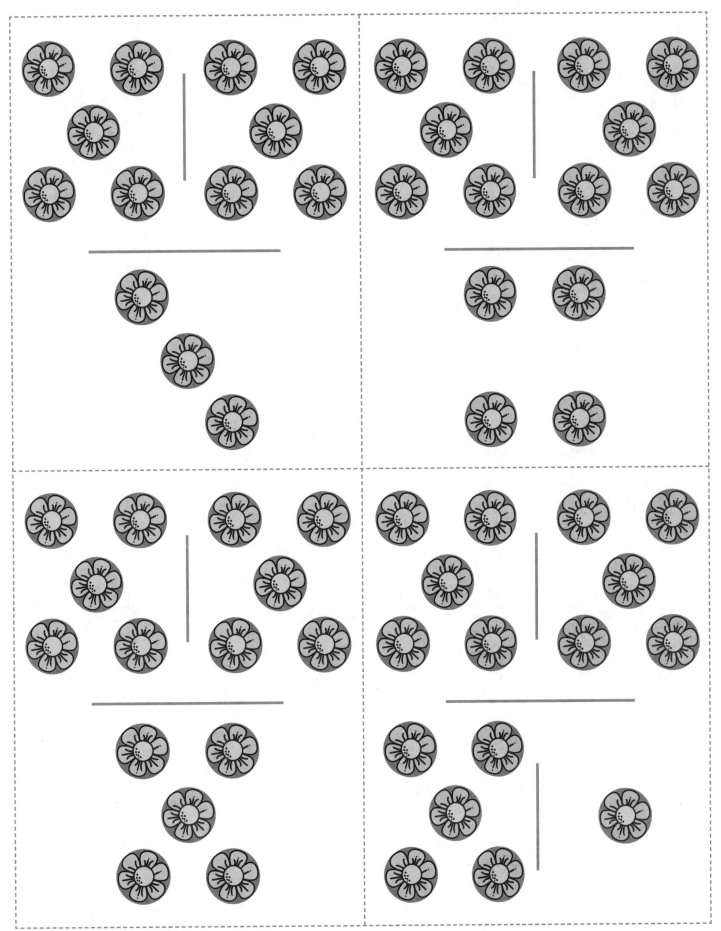

#3177 Full-Color Math Games Pre K–K

Field of Flowers Flower Counting Cards

Field
of
Flowers

Field
of
Flowers

Field
of
Flowers

Field
of
Flowers

Field of Flowers Flower Counting Cards

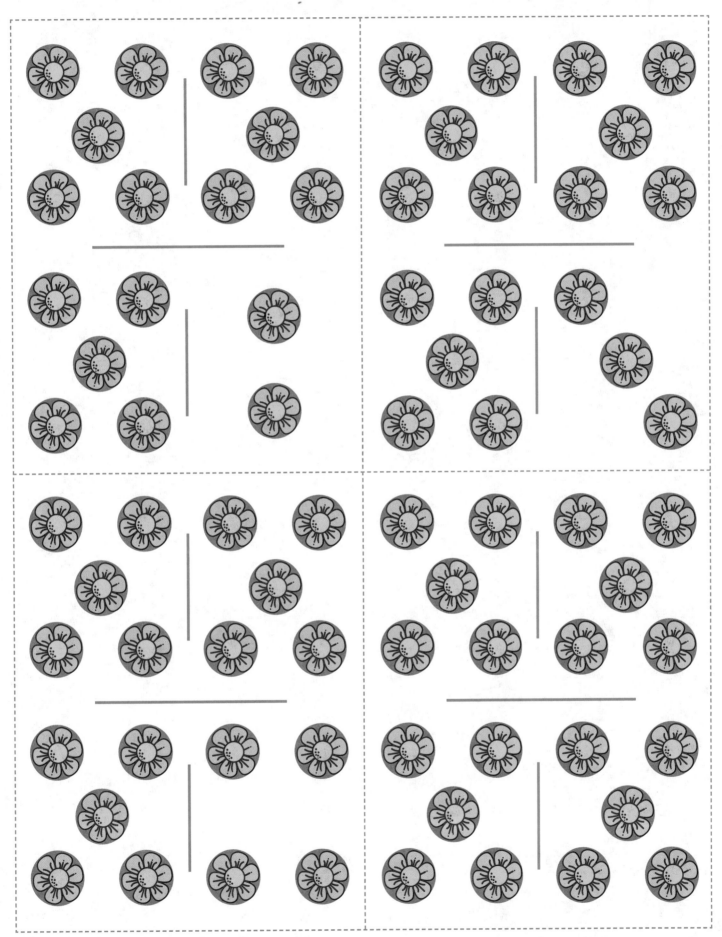

Field of Flowers Flower Counting Cards

Field
of
Flowers

Field
of
Flowers

Field
of
Flowers

Field
of
Flowers

Buzzing Bees

Number Recognition and Counting

Objective: Students will recognize numbers and count sets of objects (1–20) using one-to-one correspondence.

Preparation

1. Assemble and laminate the Buzzing Bees Game Board (pages 62 and 63).

2. Laminate and cut out the Buzzing Bees Honey Pots Counting Cards (pages 65, 67, 69, 71, and 73).

3. Laminate and cut out the Bee Cover Ups (page 75).

4. Laminate the Buzzing Bees Directions (page 59).

5. Store the Buzzing Bees Honey Pots Counting Cards and the Bee Cover Ups in a resealable storage bag. Label the bag with the game name label (page 175).

Buzzing Bees Directions

Materials

Buzzing Bees Game Board

Buzzing Bees Honey Pots Counting Cards

Buzzing Bees Bee Cover Ups

How to Play the Game

2–4 players

1. Shuffle the honey pots counting cards and place them facedown beside the Buzzing Bees game board.

2. Divide the bees among the players.

3. Take turns drawing a honey pots counting card and counting the number of honey pots shown on the card. Use a bee to cover the correct answer on the Buzzing Bees game board.

4. Continue taking turns until all the numbers on the Buzzing Bees game board have been covered.

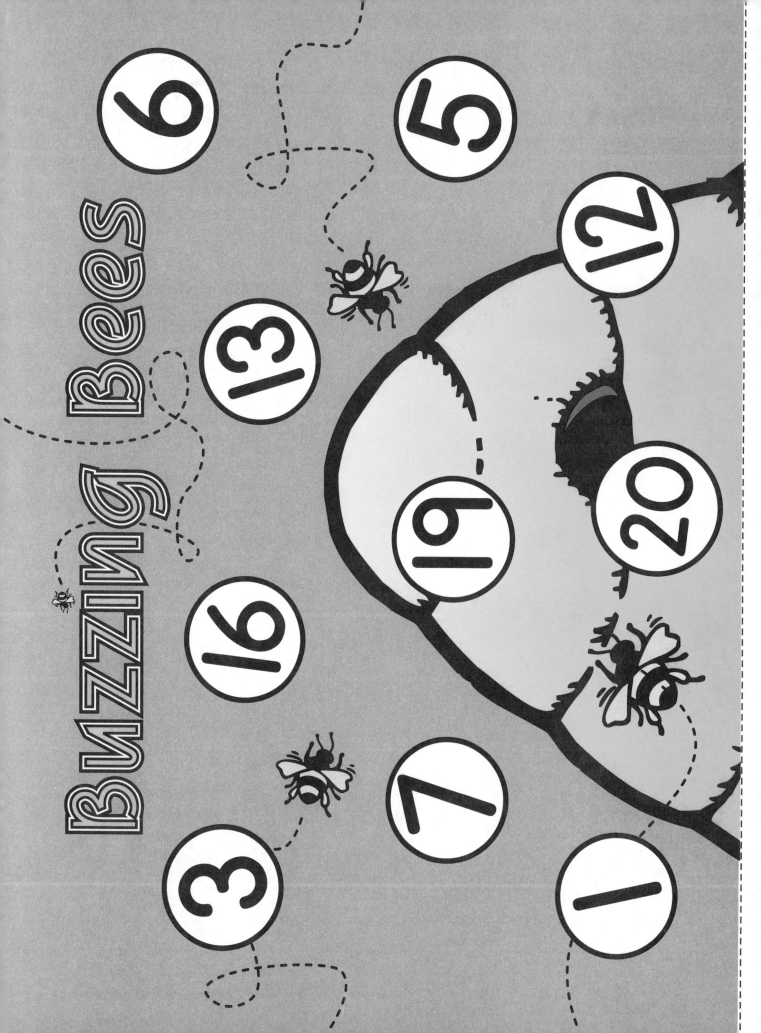

Buzzing Bees Honey Counting Cards

#3177 Full-Color Math Games Pre K–K

Buzzing
Bees

Buzzing
Bees

Buzzing
Bees

Buzzing
Bees

Buzzing Bees Honey Counting Cards

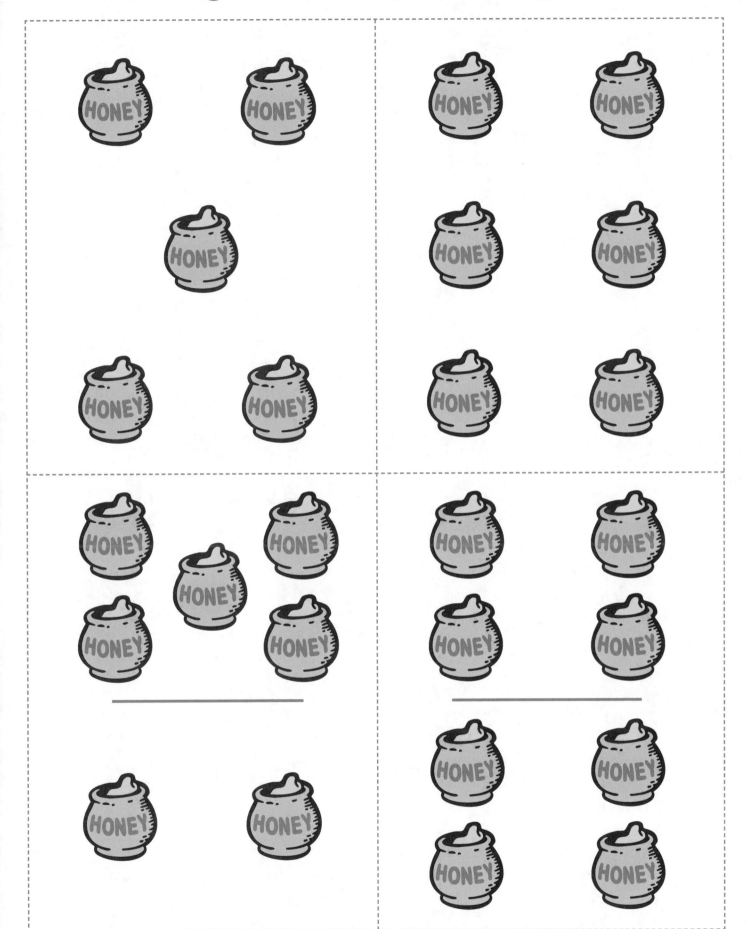

Buzzing
Bees

Buzzing
Bees

Buzzing
Bees

Buzzing
Bees

Buzzing Bees Honey Counting Cards

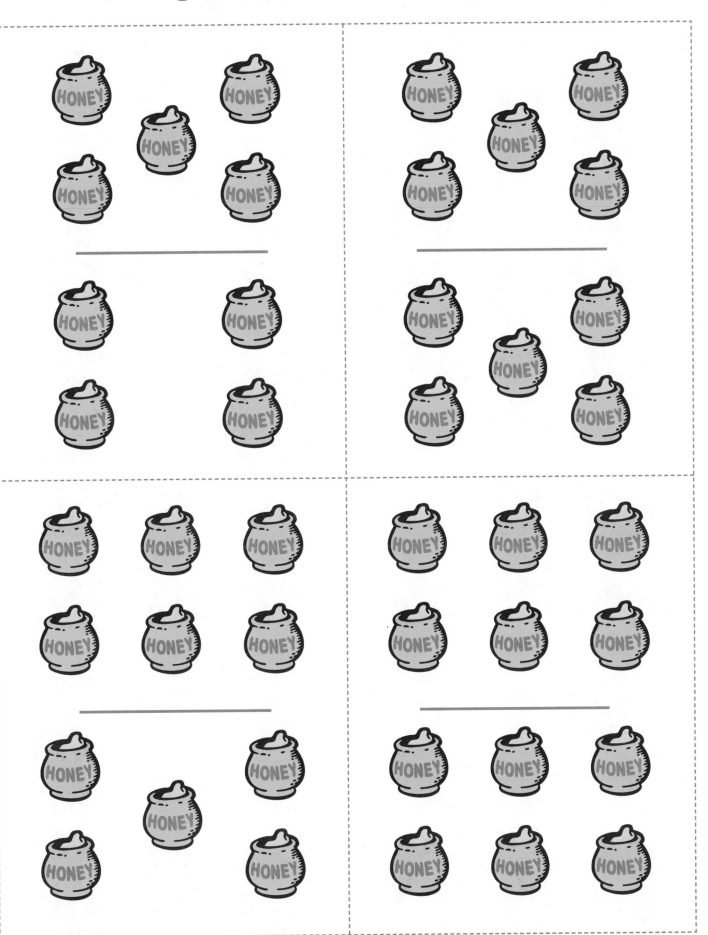

Buzzing
Bees

Buzzing
Bees

Buzzing
Bees

Buzzing
Bees

Buzzing Bees Honey Counting Cards

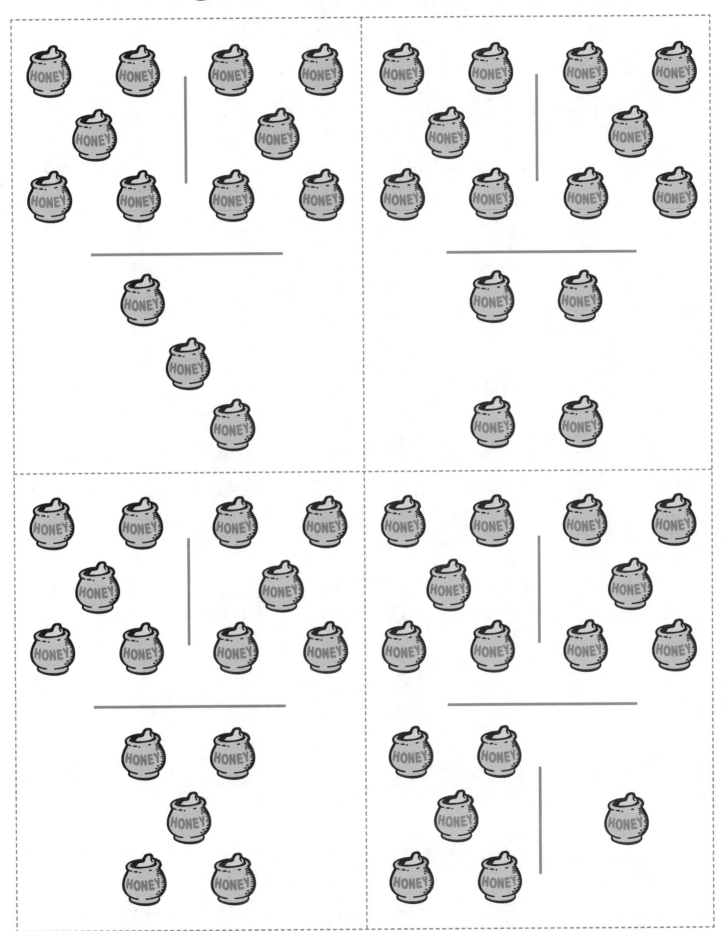

Buzzing Bees Honey Counting Cards

Buzzing
Bees

Buzzing
Bees

Buzzing
Bees

Buzzing
Bees

72

Buzzing Bees Honey Counting Cards

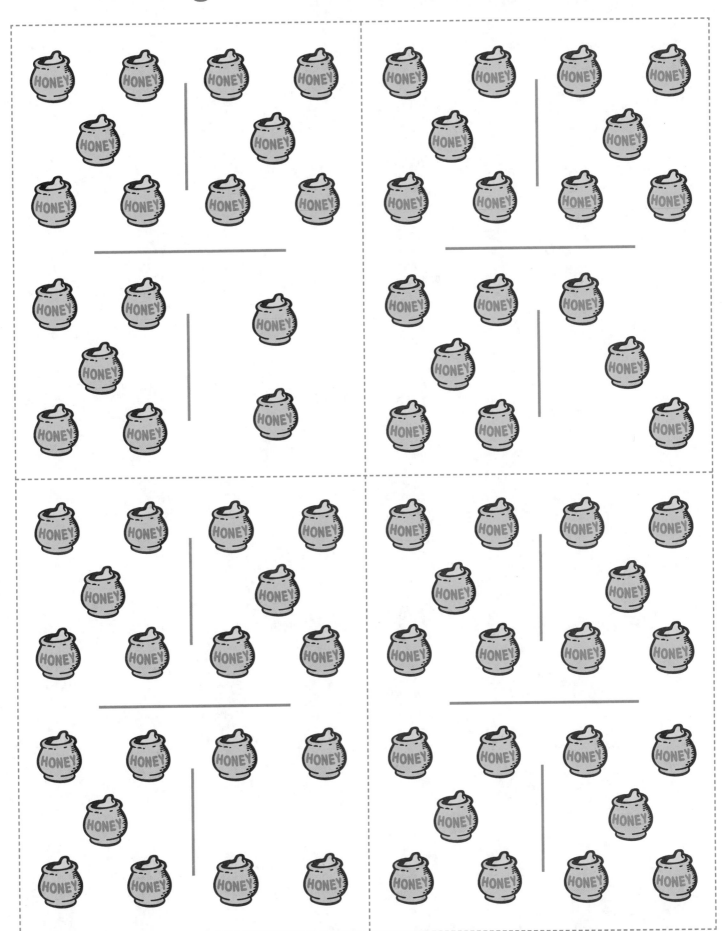

Buzzing
Bees

Buzzing
Bees

Buzzing
Bees

Buzzing
Bees

Searching for Seashells

Coin Value

Objective: Students will identify coins by name and value (penny, nickel, dime, quarter).

Preparation

1. Assemble and laminate the Searching for Seashells Game Board (pages 80 and 81).
2. Laminate and cut out the Searching for Seashells Coin Cards (page 83).
3. Laminate and cut out the Seashell Cover Ups (page 85).
4. Laminate the Searching for Seashells Directions (page 77).
5. Store the Searching for Seashells Coin Cards and the Seashell Cover Ups in a resealable storage bag. Label the bag with the game name label (page 175).

Searching for Seashells Directions

Materials

Searching for Seashells Game Board

Searching for Seashells Coin Cards

Searching for Seashells Seashell Cover Ups

How to Play the Game

2–4 players

1. Shuffle the coin cards and place them facedown beside the Searching for Seashells game board.
2. Divide the seashells among the players.
3. Take turns drawing a coin card and covering the matching money amount on the game board with a sea shell.
4. Continue taking turns until all the money amounts on the Searching for Seashells game board have been covered.

Searching for SeaShells

Searching for Seashells Coin Cards

Searching for Seashells Coin Cards

Searching for Seashells

Searching for Seashells

Searching for Seashells

Searching for Seashells

Searching for Seashells

Searching for Seashells

Searching for Seashells

Searching for Seashells

Searching for Seashells

Searching for Seashells

Searching for Seashells

Searching for Seashells

Searching for Seashells

Searching for Seashells

Searching for Seashells

Searching for Seashells

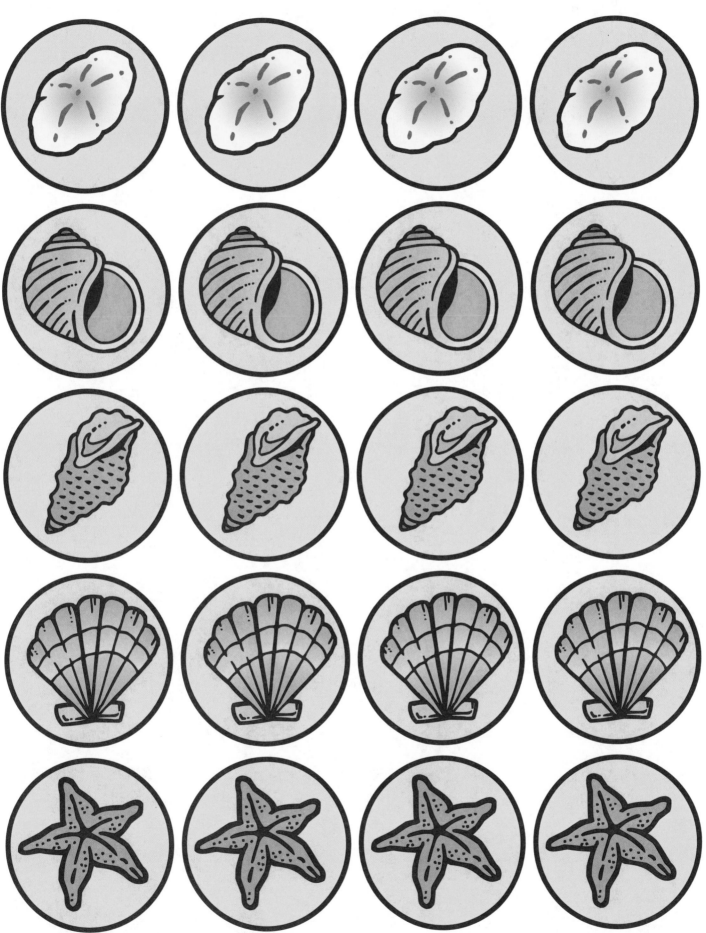

Lemonade Stand

Coin Value

Objective: Students will identify coins by name and value (penny, nickel, dime, quarter).

Preparation

1. Assemble and laminate the Lemonade Stand Game Board (pages 90 and 91).

2. Laminate and cut out the Lemonade Stand Money Cards (page 93).

3. Laminate and cut out the Lemon Cover Ups (page 95).

4. Laminate the Lemonade Stand Directions (page 87).

5. Store the Lemonade Stand Money Cards and the Lemon Cover Ups in a resealable storage bag. Label the bag with the game name label (page 175).

Lemonade Stand Directions

Materials

Lemonade Stand Game Board

Lemonade Stand Money Cards

Lemonade Stand Lemon Cover Ups

How to Play the Game

2–4 players

1. Shuffle the money cards and place them facedown beside the Lemonade Stand game board.

2. Divide the lemons among the players.

3. Take turns drawing a money card and covering the matching coin on the game board with a lemon.

4. Continue taking turns until all the coins on the Lemonade Stand game board have been covered.

Lemonade Stand
Money Cards

1¢	1¢	1¢	1¢
5¢	5¢	5¢	5¢
10¢	10¢	10¢	10¢
25¢	25¢	25¢	25¢

Lemonade Stand
Money Cards

Lemonade Stand   Lemonade Stand   Lemonade Stand   Lemonade Stand

Lemonade Stand   Lemonade Stand   Lemonade Stand   Lemonade Stand

Lemonade Stand   Lemonade Stand   Lemonade Stand   Lemonade Stand

Lemonade Stand   Lemonade Stand   Lemonade Stand   Lemonade Stand

#3177 Full-Color Math Games Pre K–K

Sand Treasures

Coin Value

Objective: Students will identify coins by name and value (penny, nickel, dime, quarter).

Preparation

1. Assemble and laminate the Sand Treasures Game Board (pages 100 and 101).

2. Laminate and cut out the Sand Treasures Money Cards (page 103).

3. Laminate and cut out the Sand Pail Cover Ups (page 105).

4. Laminate the Sand Treasures Directions (page 97).

5. Store the Sand Treasures Money Cards and Sand Pail Cover Ups in a resealable storage bag. Label the bag with the game name label (page 175).

Sand Treasures Directions

Materials

Sand Treasures Game Board

Sand Treasures Money Cards

Sand Treasures Sand Pail Cover Ups

How to Play the Game

2–4 players

1. Shuffle the money cards and place them facedown beside the Sand Treasures game board.

2. Divide the sand pails among the players.

3. Take turns drawing a money card and covering the matching coin on the game board with a sand pail.

4. Continue taking turns until all the coins on the Sand Treasures game board have been covered.

Sand Treasures Money Cards

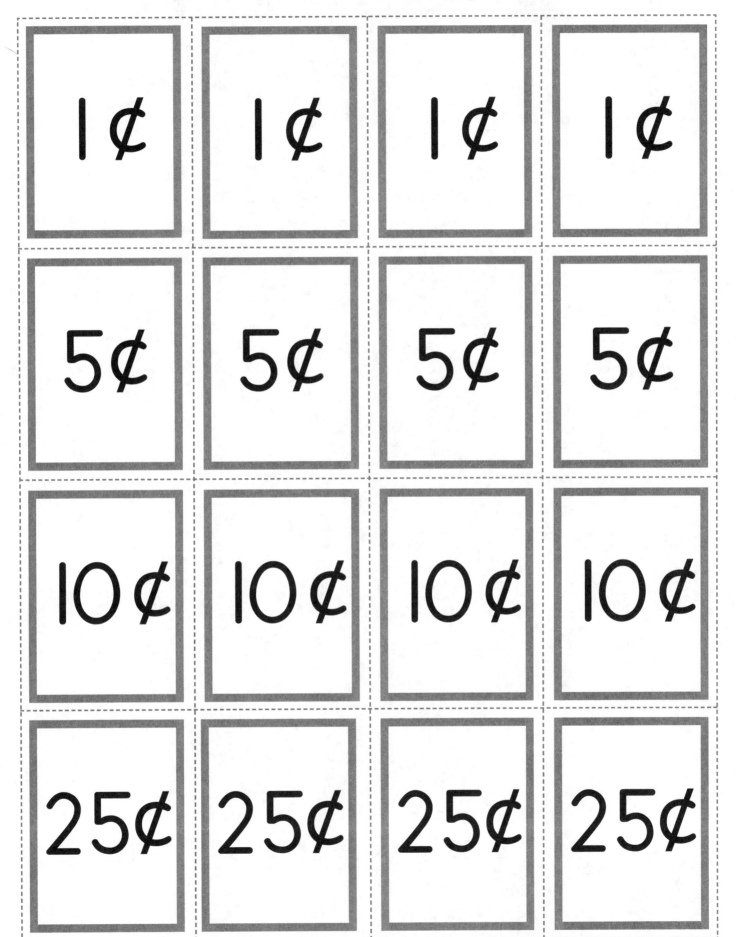

Sand Treasures Money Cards

Sand Treasures

Sand Treasures

Sand Treasures

Sand Treasures

Sand Treasures

Sand Treasures

Sand Treasures

Sand Treasures

Sand Treasures

Sand Treasures

Sand Treasures

Sand Treasures

Sand Treasures

Sand Treasures

Sand Treasures

Sand Treasures

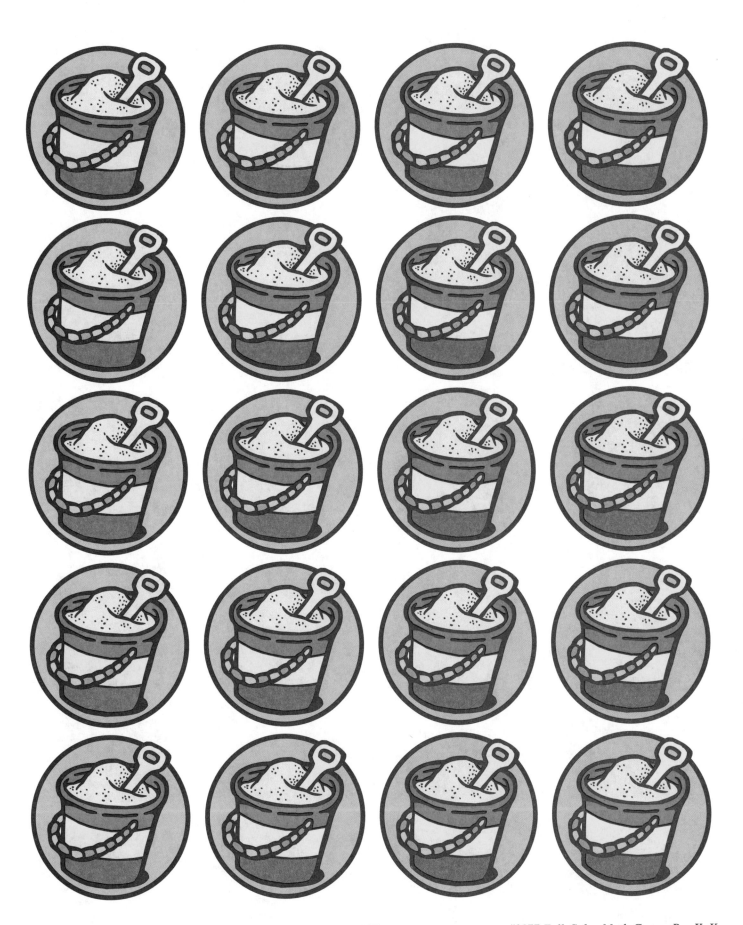

Scuba Dive

Coin Value

Objective: Students will identify coins by name and value (penny, nickel, dime, quarter).

Preparation

1. Assemble and laminate the Scuba Dive Game Board (pages 110 and 111).

2. Laminate and cut out the Scuba Dive Coin Cards (page 113).

3. Laminate and cut out the Scuba Dive Mask and Fin Cover Ups (page 115).

4. Laminate the Scuba Dive Directions (page 107).

5. Store the Scuba Dive Coin Cards and the Scuba Dive Mask and Fin Cover Ups in a resealable storage bag. Label the bag with the game name label (page 175).

Scuba Dive Directions

Materials

Scuba Dive Game Board

Scuba Dive Coin Cards

Scuba Dive Mask and Fin Cover Ups

How to Play the Game

2–4 players

1. Shuffle the coin cards and place them facedown beside the Scuba Dive game board.

2. Divide the masks and fins among the players.

3. Take turns drawing a coin card and covering the matching money amount on the game board with a mask or a fin.

4. Continue taking turns until all the money amounts on the Scuba Dive game board have been covered.

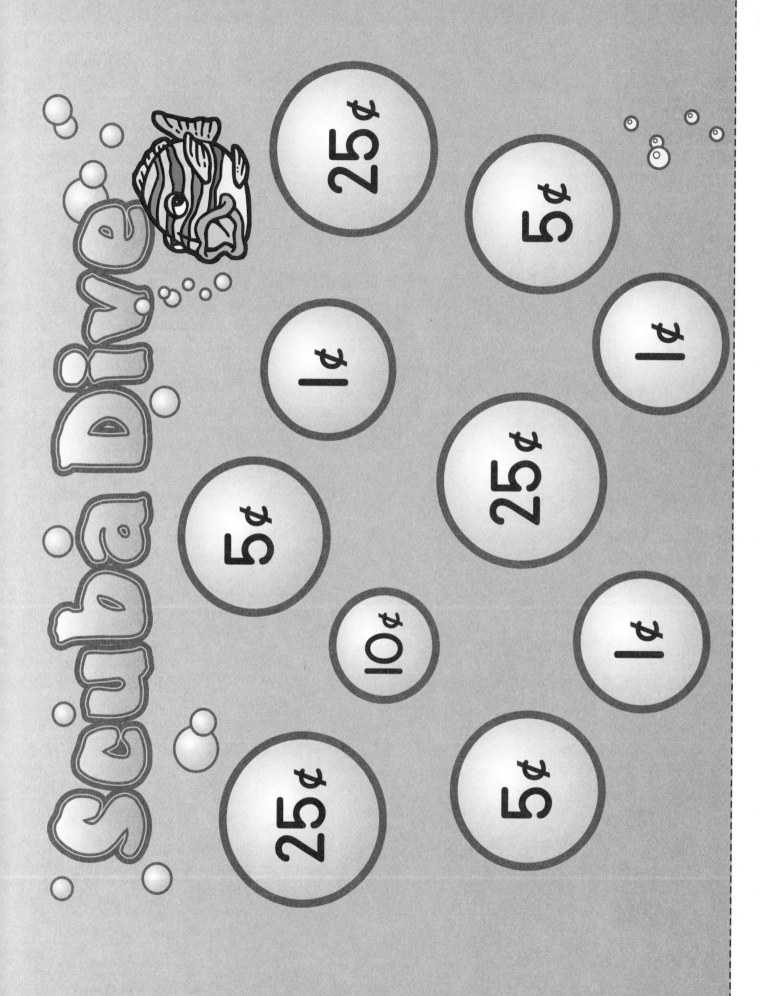

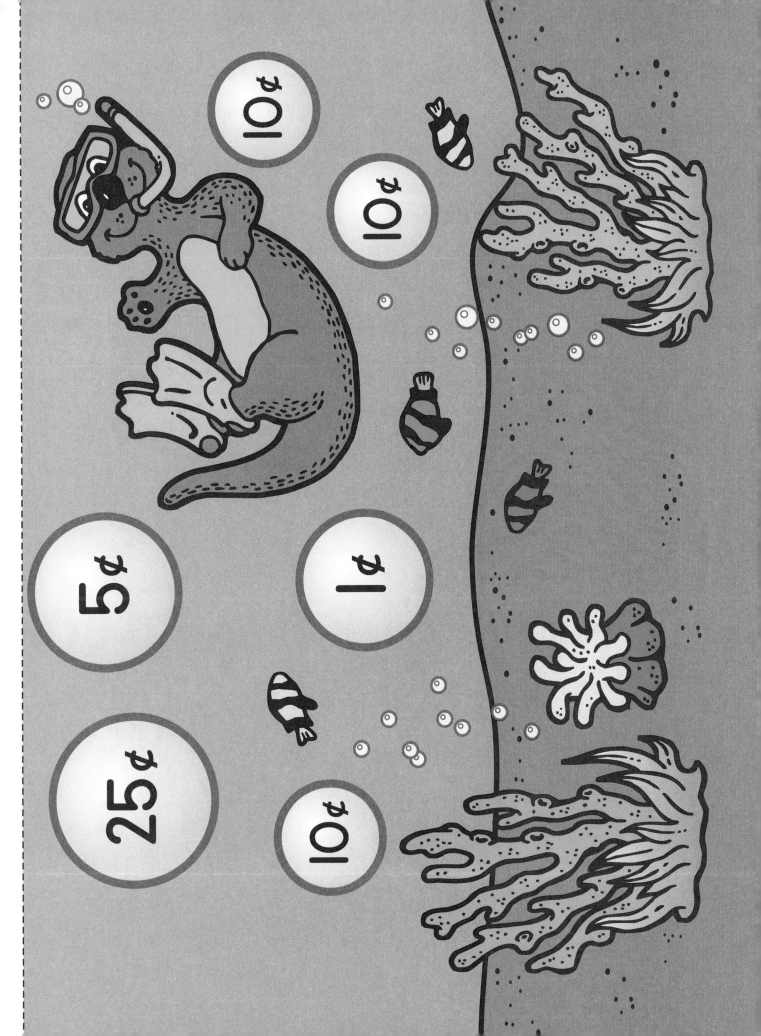

Scuba Dive Coin Cards

Scuba Dive Coin Cards

Scuba

Dive

Scuba

Dive

Scuba

Dive

Scuba

Dive

Scuba

Dive

Scuba

Dive

Scuba

Dive

Scuba

Dive

Scuba

Dive

Scuba

Dive

Scuba

Dive

Scuba

Dive

Scuba

Dive

Scuba

Dive

Scuba

Dive

Scuba

Dive

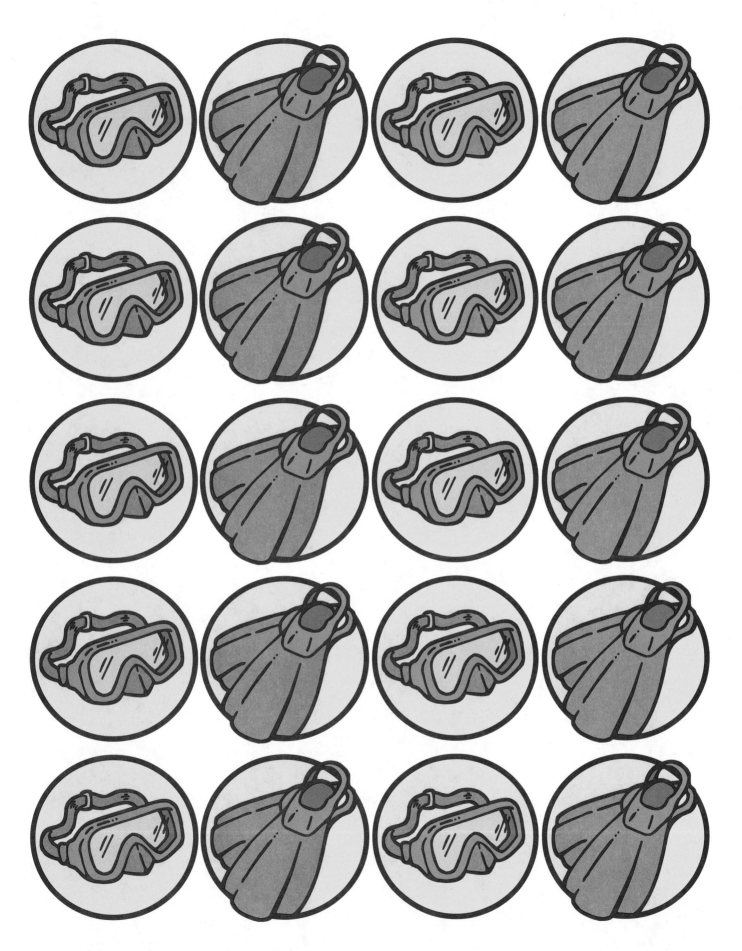

Cuddles the Cow

Number Sequence 1-20

Objective: Students will recognize numbers (1–20) and identify the missing number in a sequence of numbers.

Preparation

1. Assemble and laminate the Cuddles the Cow Game Board (pages 120 and 121).

2. Laminate and cut out the Cuddles the Cow Sequencing Cards (pages 123, 125, and 127).

3. Laminate and cut out the Cow Spot Cover Ups (page 129). The cow spots may be cut out on the lines provided (as cards) or on the spot outlines.

4. Laminate the Cuddles the Cow Directions (page 117).

5. Store the Cuddles the Cow Sequencing Cards and Cow Spot Cover Ups in a resealable storage bag. Label the bag with the game name label (page 175).

Cuddles the Cow Directions

Materials

Cuddles the Cow Game Board

Cuddles the Cow Sequencing Cards

Cuddles the Cow Spot Cover Ups

How to Play the Game

2–4 players

1. Shuffle the sequencing cards and place them facedown beside the Cuddles the Cow game board.

2. Divide the cow spots among the players.

3. Take turns drawing a sequencing card and identifying the missing number. Use a cow spot card to cover the answer on the Cuddles the Cow game board.

4. Continue taking turns until all the numbers on the Cuddles the Cow game board have been covered.

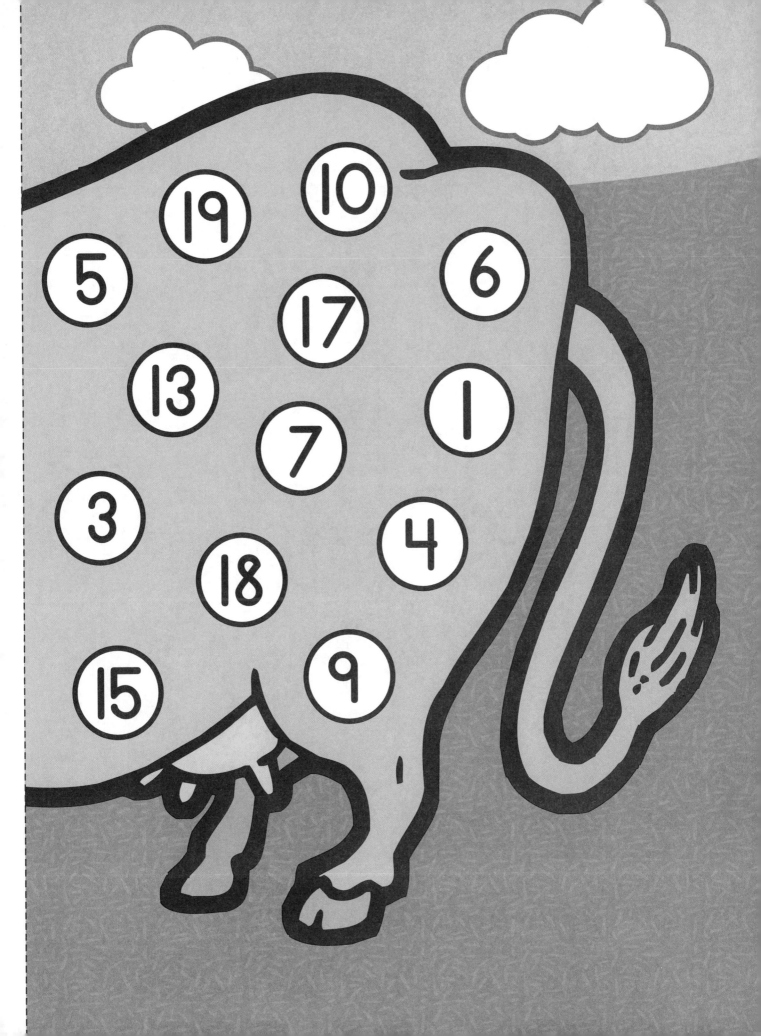

Cuddles the Cow Sequencing Cards

_____, 2, 3

0, 1, _____

2, _____, 4

_____, 5, 6

3, 4, _____

5, _____, 7

_____, 8, 9

6, 7, _____

Cuddles the Cow Sequencing Cards

Cuddles
the
Cow

Cuddles
the
Cow

Cuddles
the
Cow

Cuddles
the
Cow

Cuddles
the
Cow

Cuddles
the
Cow

Cuddles
the
Cow

Cuddles
the
Cow

Cuddles the Cow Sequencing Cards

8, _____ , 10

_____ , 11, 12

9, 10, _____

11, _____ , 13

_____ , 14, 15

12, 13, _____

Cuddles the Cow Sequencing Cards

Cuddles
the
Cow

Cuddles
the
Cow

Cuddles
the
Cow

Cuddles
the
Cow

Cuddles
the
Cow

Cuddles
the
Cow

Cuddles
the
Cow

Cuddles
the
Cow

Cuddles the Cow Sequencing Cards

14, _____ , 16

_____ , 17, 18

15, 16, _____

17, _____ , 19

_____ , 20, 21

18, 19, _____

Cuddles the Cow Sequencing Cards

Cuddles
the
Cow

Cuddles
the
Cow

Cuddles
the
Cow

Cuddles
the
Cow

Cuddles
the
Cow

Cuddles
the
Cow

Cuddles
the
Cow

Cuddles
the
Cow

Tracy the Turtle

Number Sequence 1-20

Objective Students will recognize numbers (1–20) and identify the missing number in a sequence of numbers.

Preparation

1. Assemble and laminate the Tracy the Turtle Game Board (pages 134 and 135).

2. Laminate and cut out the Tracy the Turtle Sequencing Cards (pages 137, 139, and 141).

3. Laminate and cut out the Turtle Spot Cover Ups (page 143). The turtle spots may be cut out on the lines provided (as cards) or on the spot outlines.

4. Laminate the Tracy the Turtle Directions (page 131).

5. Store the Tracy the Turtle Sequencing Cards and the Turtle Spot Cover Ups in a resealable storage bag. Label the bag with the game name label (page 175).

Tracy the Turtle Directions

Materials

Tracy the Turtle Game Board

Tracy the Turtle Sequencing Cards

Tracy the Turtle Spot Cover Ups

How to Play the Game

2–4 players

1. Shuffle the sequencing cards and place them facedown beside the Tracy the Turtle game board.

2. Divide the turtle spots among the players.

3. Take turns drawing a sequencing card and identifying the missing number. Use a turtle spot to cover the answer on the Tracy the Turtle game board.

4. Continue taking turns until all the numbers on the Tracy the Turtle game board have been covered.

132

TRACY the TURTLE

13

7

19

15

2

Tracy the Turtle Sequencing Cards

0, _____, 2

_____, 3, 4

1, 2, _____

_____, 5, 6

4, _____, 6

4, 5, _____

6, _____, 8

_____, 9, 10

Tracy the Turtle Sequencing Cards

Tracy
the
Turtle

Tracy
the
Turtle

Tracy
the
Turtle

Tracy
the
Turtle

Tracy
the
Turtle

Tracy
the
Turtle

Tracy
the
Turtle

Tracy
the
Turtle

Tracy the Turtle Sequencing Cards

7, 8, _____

9, _____, 11

_____, 12, 13

10, 11, _____

12, _____, 14

_____, 15, 16

Tracy the Turtle Sequencing Cards

Tracy
the
Turtle

Tracy
the
Turtle

Tracy
the
Turtle

Tracy
the
Turtle

Tracy
the
Turtle

Tracy
the
Turtle

Tracy
the
Turtle

Tracy
the
Turtle

Tracy the Turtle Sequencing Cards

13, 14, _____

15, _____, 17

_____, 18, 19

16, 17, _____

18, _____, 20

_____, 21, 22

Tracy the Turtle Sequencing Cards

Tracy
the
Turtle

Tracy
the
Turtle

Tracy
the
Turtle

Tracy
the
Turtle

Tracy
the
Turtle

Tracy
the
Turtle

Tracy
the
Turtle

Tracy
the
Turtle

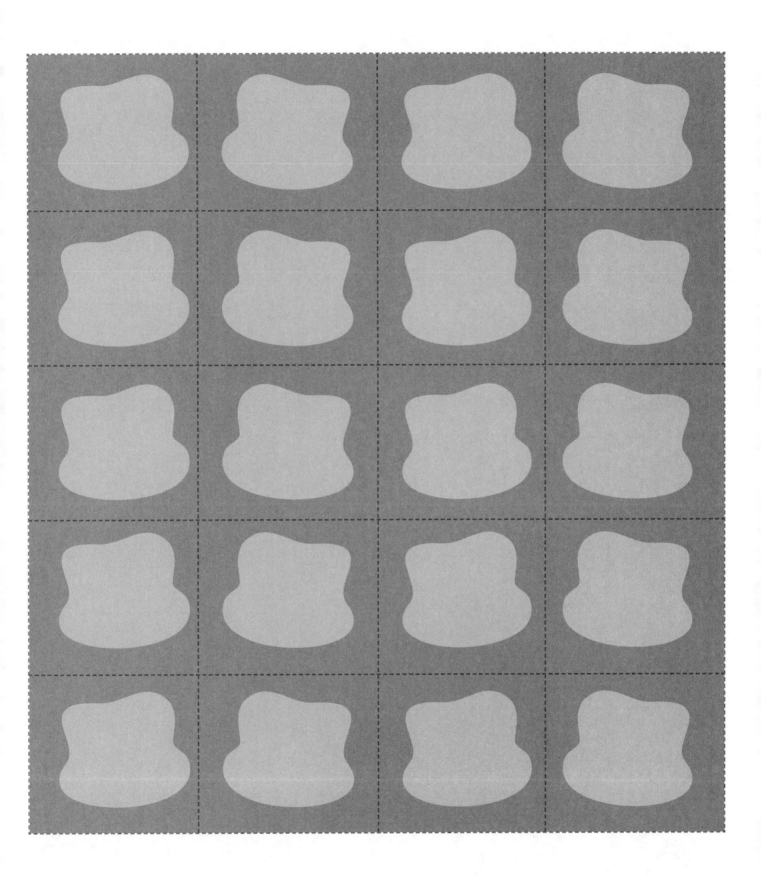

Tommy the Tiger

Number Sequence 1–20

Objective: Students will recognize numbers (1–20) and identify the missing number in a sequence of numbers.

Preparation

1. Assemble and laminate the Tommy the Tiger Game Board (pages 148 and 149).

2. Laminate and cut out the Tommy the Tiger Number Cards (pages 151, 153, and 155).

3. Laminate and cut out the Tiger Stripe Cover Ups (page 157). The Tiger stripes must be cut out on the picture outlines to fit on the game board.

4. Laminate the Tommy the Tiger Directions (page 145).

5. Store the Tommy the Tiger Number Cards and the Tiger Stripe Cover Ups in a resealable storage bag. Label the bag with the game name label (page 175).

Tommy the Tiger Directions

Materials

Tommy the Tiger Game Board

Tommy the Tiger Number Cards

Tommy the Tiger Stripe Cover Ups

How to Play the Game

2–4 players

1. Shuffle the number cards and place them facedown beside the Tommy the Tiger game board.

2. Divide the tiger stripes among the players.

3. Take turns drawing a number card and identifying the number. Find the number sequence on the game board where the number should go and use a tiger stripe to cover it.

4. Continue taking turns until all the number sequences on the Tommy the Tiger game board have been covered.

147

THE TIGER
___, 18, 19
18, ___, 20
___, 5, 6
___, 9, 10
___, 15, 16
___, 21, 22
16, 17, ___
15, ___, 17
13, 14, ___
___, 3, 4
10, 11, ___
4, 5, ___
9, ___ 11

Tommy the Tiger Number Cards

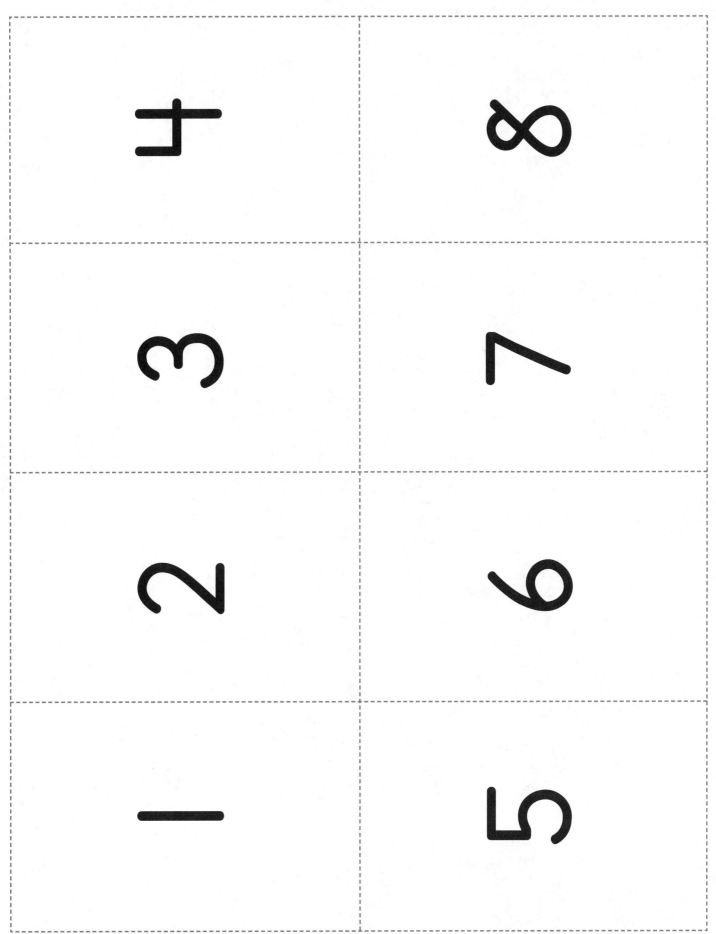

Tommy the Tiger Number Cards

Tommy the Tiger

Tommy the Tiger

Tommy the Tiger

Tommy the Tiger

Tommy the Tiger

Tommy the Tiger

Tommy the Tiger

Tommy the Tiger

Tommy the Tiger Number Cards

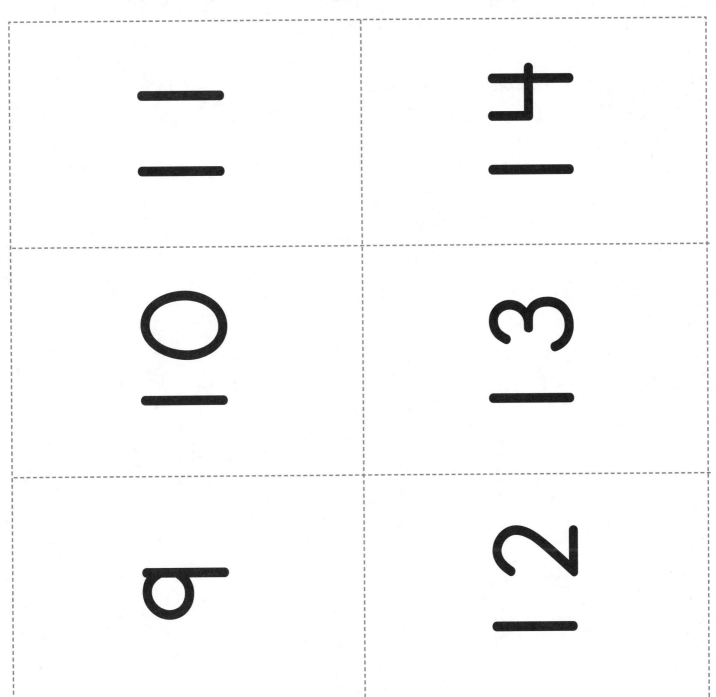

Tommy the Tiger Number Cards

Tommy the Tiger

Tommy the Tiger

Tommy the Tiger

Tommy the Tiger

Tommy the Tiger

Tommy the Tiger

Tommy the Tiger

Tommy the Tiger

154

Tommy the Tiger Number Cards

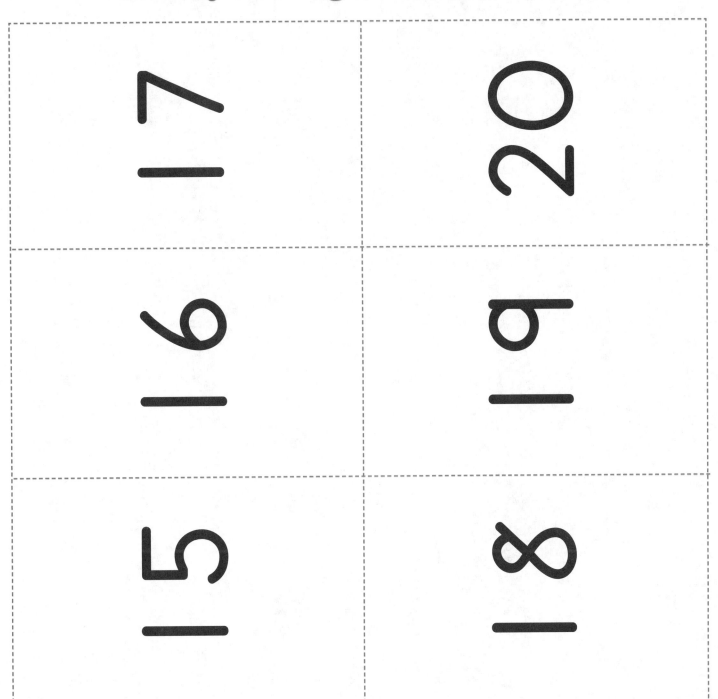

Tommy the Tiger Number Cards

Tommy the Tiger

Tommy the Tiger

Tommy the Tiger

Tommy the Tiger

Tommy the Tiger

Tommy the Tiger

Tommy the Tiger

Tommy the Tiger

#3177 Full-Color Math Games Pre K–K

Zack the Zebra

Number Sequence 1–20

Objective: Students will recognize numbers (1–20) and identify the missing number in a sequence of numbers.

Preparation

1. Assemble and laminate the Zack the Zebra Game Board (pages 162 and 163).

2. Laminate and cut out the Zack the Zebra Number Cards (pages 165, 167, and 169).

3. Laminate and cut out the Zebra Stripe Cover Ups (page 171). The zebra stripes must be cut out on the picture outlines to fit on the game board.

4. Laminate the Zack the Zebra Directions (page 159).

5. Store the Zack the Zebra Number Cards and the Zebra Stripe Cover Ups in a resealable storage bag. Label the bag with the game name label (page 175).

Zack the Zebra Directions

Materials

Zack the Zebra Game Board

Zack the Zebra Number Cards

Zack the Zebra Stripe Cover Ups

How to Play the Game

2–4 players

1. Shuffle the number cards and place them facedown beside the Zack the Zebra game board.

2. Divide the zebra stripes among the players.

3. Take turns drawing a number card and identifying the number. Find the number sequence on the game board where the number should go and use a zebra stripe to cover it.

4. Continue taking turns until all the number sequences on the Zack the Zebra game board have been covered.

ZACK the

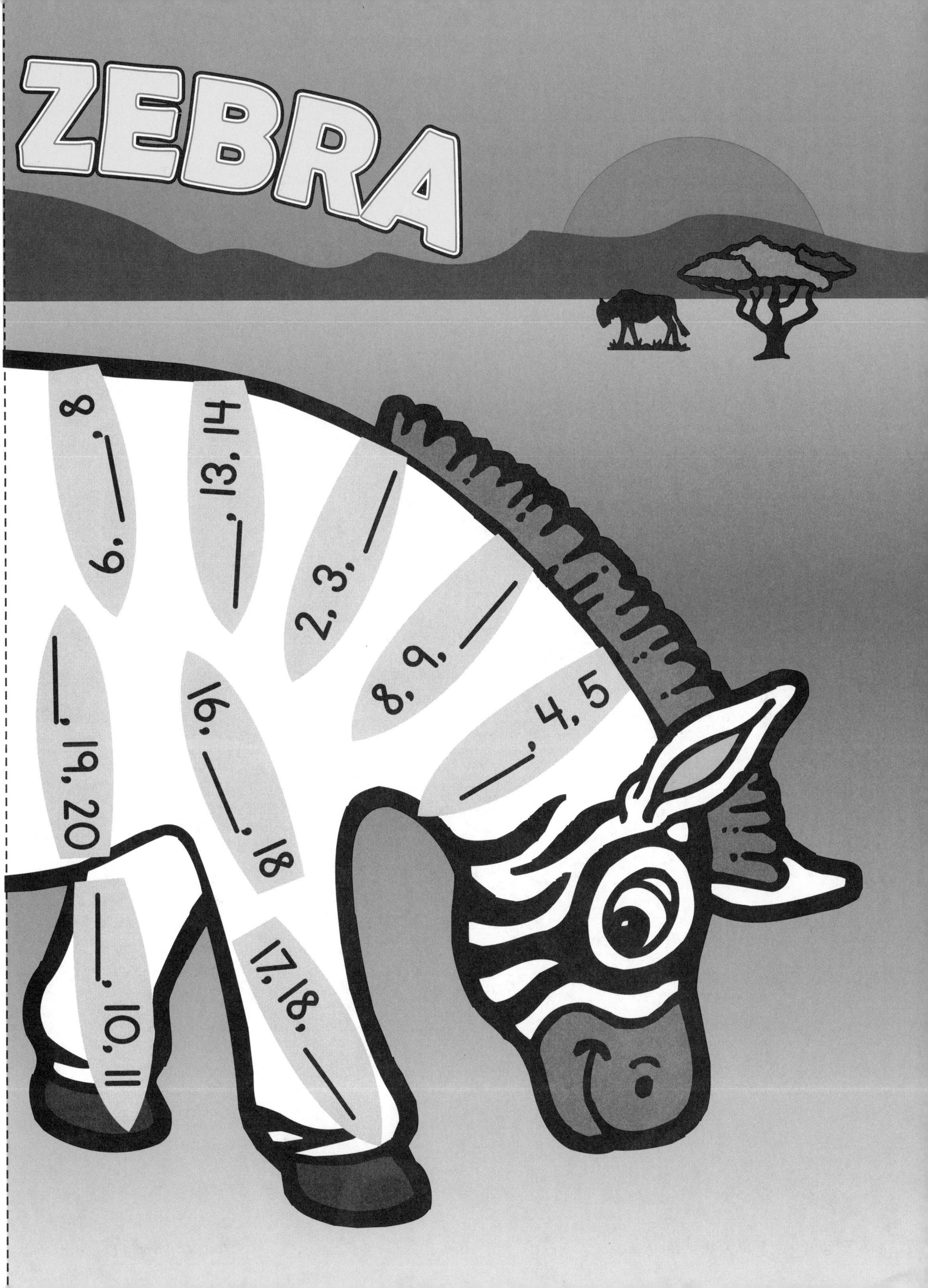
ZEBRA
6, ___, 8
___, 13, 14
2, 3, ___
8, 9, ___
___, 4, 5
___, 19, 20
16, ___, 18
___, 10, 11
17, 18, ___

Zack the Zebra Number Cards

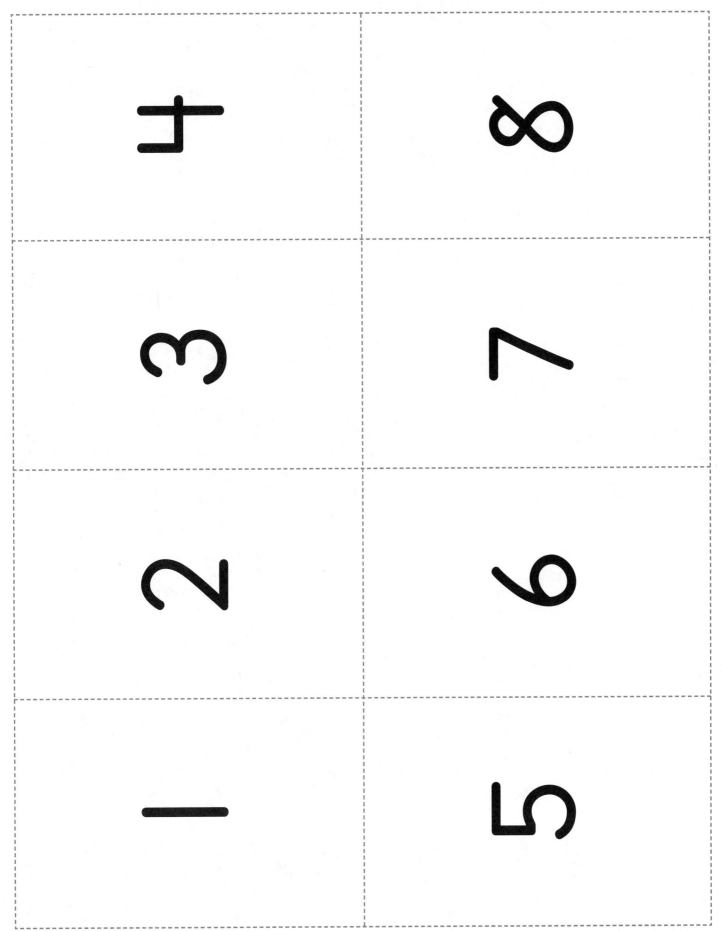

Zack the Zebra Number Cards

Zack

the

Zebra

Zack

the

Zebra

Zack

the

Zebra

Zack

the

Zebra

Zack

the

Zebra

Zack

the

Zebra

Zack

the

Zebra

Zack

the

Zebra

Zack the Zebra Number Cards

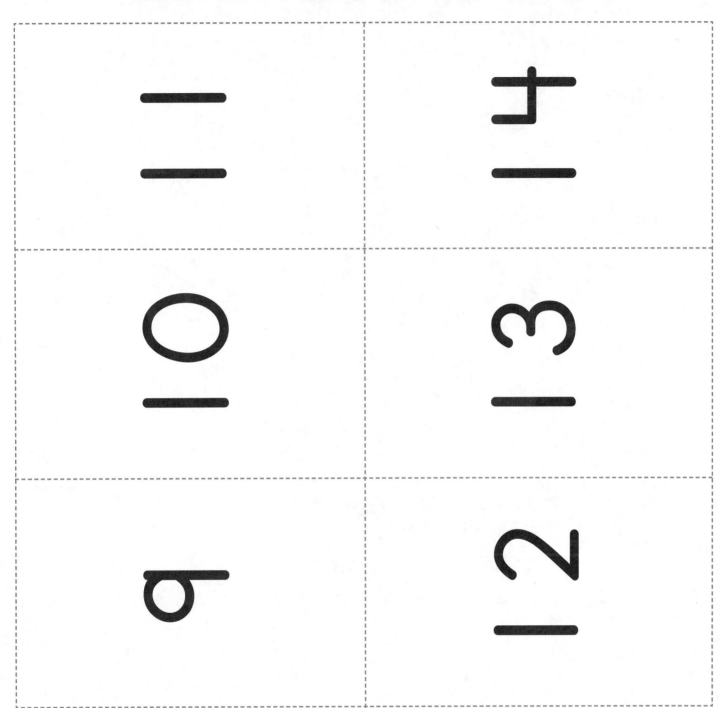

Zack the Zebra Number Cards

Zack the Zebra

Zack the Zebra

Zack the Zebra

Zack the Zebra

Zack the Zebra

Zack the Zebra

Zack the Zebra

Zack the Zebra